My
SHOWS
&
PLAYS

WORKBOOK FOR ACTORS, DANCERS
AND MUSICAL THEATRE PERFORMERS

MT THEATRE GUIDES & JOURNALS

Forthcoming...

Look out on Amazon for further titles in the MT Theatre Guides and Journals series:

So You Want to go into Performing Arts... The Insider's Guide to Training & Careers For Dancers, Singers, Actors and Musical Theatre Performers.

(Due: late 2024) A guide for teens considering going into the industry — and for their parents, including interviews with West End performers and industry insiders.

How to Have a Great Career in Performing Arts: Tips, Hacks & Advice from Professional Actors, Dancers & Musical Theatre Performers.

(Due: 2025) After drama school or dance college.... what next?
Case studies with life lessons — everyone's path is different!

My Big Show Scrapbook

(Due: late 2024) A memory book for theatre kids aged 8-12,
to record their shows and performances

A Dancer's Progress Journal

(Due: 2025) Record memories of your shows, log festival and exam results, keep track of your progress, make notes on how you can improve. A wonderful gift for young dancers.

Inspiration

"To practice any art, no matter how well or badly, is a way to make your soul grow. So do it."

– Kurt Vonnegut, celebrated American author and Nazi prison camp survivor (Slaughterhouse-Five)

"Sometimes you can have the smallest role in the smallest production and still have a big impact."

— Neil Patrick Harris, actor (How I Met Your Mother).

"The play is not in the words, it's in you!"

– Stella Adler, American actor, producer, director and teacher. Founder of the Stella Adler Studio of Acting, NYC.

"Lots and lots of things scare me but you just get on with it. Fright can transform into petrol, you just have to use it to your advantage."

— Dame Judi Dench, multi award-winning British actor, star of stage and screen.

"You've gotta be original. Because if you're like someone else, what do they need you for?"

– Bernadette Peters, multi award-winning star of stage, screen and Broadway.

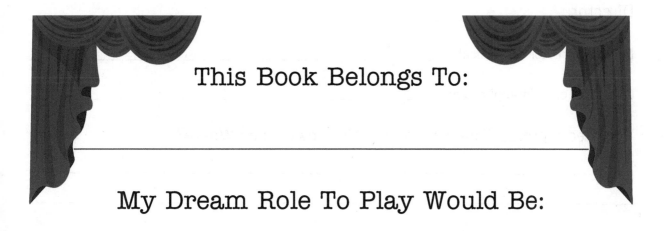

This Book Belongs To:

_____

My Dream Role To Play Would Be:

_____

The Show

Name of Show: _____

Date/s: _____

Theatre/Venue: _____

Director: _____

Musical Director (if applicable): _____

Choreographer (if applicable): _____

Watched a professional version of this show? When/Where?

_____

_____

_____

Role/s I auditioned for: _____

Anything of note about auditioning:

_____

_____

_____

_____

Character/s I played: _____

Notes on/any particular memories of the rehearsal process:

_____

_____

_____

_____

Reflections

What I learned from this director (notes I was given):

_____

_____

_____

_____

What I learned from others in the cast:

_____

_____

_____

_____

My assessment of this show and what it was memorable for:

_____

_____

_____

_____

Would I like to be in a future production of this show?   **YES / NO**

If yes, which character/s would I like to play?

_____

_____

Anything I need to work on to achieve that:

_____

_____

_____

Memories

(Photos / tickets / cast list / cuttings from the programme)

(Photos / tickets / cast list /
cuttings from the programme)

The Show

Name of Show: _____

Date/s: _____

Theatre/Venue: _____

Director: _____

Musical Director (if applicable): _____

Choreographer (if applicable): _____

Watched a professional version of this show? When/Where?

_____

_____

_____

Role/s I auditioned for: _____

Anything of note about auditioning:

_____

_____

_____

_____

Character/s I played: _____

Notes on/any particular memories of the rehearsal process:

_____

_____

_____

_____

Reflections

What I learned from this director (notes I was given):

_____

_____

_____

_____

What I learned from others in the cast:

_____

_____

_____

_____

My assessment of this show and what it was memorable for:

_____

_____

_____

_____

Would I like to be in a future production of this show?   **YES / NO**

If yes, which character/s would I like to play?

_____

_____

Anything I need to work on to achieve that:

_____

_____

_____

Memories

(Photos / tickets / cast list / cuttings from the programme)

(Photos / tickets / cast list / cuttings from the programme)

The Show

Name of Show: _____

Date/s: _____

Theatre/Venue: _____

Director: _____

Musical Director (if applicable): _____

Choreographer (if applicable): _____

Watched a professional version of this show? When/Where?

_____

_____

_____

Role/s I auditioned for: _____

Anything of note about auditioning:

_____

_____

_____

_____

Character/s I played: _____

Notes on/any particular memories of the rehearsal process:

_____

_____

_____

_____

Reflections

What I learned from this director (notes I was given):

_____

_____

_____

_____

What I learned from others in the cast:

_____

_____

_____

_____

My assessment of this show and what it was memorable for:

_____

_____

_____

_____

Would I like to be in a future production of this show?   **YES / NO**

If yes, which character/s would I like to play?

_____

_____

Anything I need to work on to achieve that:

_____

_____

_____

Memories

(Photos / tickets / cast list /
cuttings from the programme)

The Show

Name of Show: _____

Date/s: _____

Theatre/Venue: _____

Director: _____

Musical Director (if applicable): _____

Choreographer (if applicable): _____

Watched a professional version of this show? When/Where?

_____

_____

_____

Role/s I auditioned for: _____

Anything of note about auditioning:

_____

_____

_____

_____

Character/s I played: _____

Notes on/any particular memories of the rehearsal process:

_____

_____

_____

_____

Reflections

What I learned from this director (notes I was given):

_____
_____
_____
_____

What I learned from others in the cast:

_____
_____
_____
_____

My assessment of this show and what it was memorable for:

_____
_____
_____
_____

Would I like to be in a future production of this show?   **YES / NO**

If yes, which character/s would I like to play?

_____
_____

Anything I need to work on to achieve that:

_____
_____
_____

Memories

(Photos / tickets / cast list / cuttings from the programme)

The Show

Name of Show: _____

Date/s: _____

Theatre/Venue: _____

Director: _____

Musical Director (if applicable): _____

Choreographer (if applicable): _____

Watched a professional version of this show? When/Where?

_____

_____

_____

Role/s I auditioned for: _____

Anything of note about auditioning:

_____

_____

_____

_____

Character/s I played: _____

Notes on/any particular memories of the rehearsal process:

_____

_____

_____

_____

Reflections

What I learned from this director (notes I was given):

_____
_____
_____
_____

What I learned from others in the cast:

_____
_____
_____
_____

My assessment of this show and what it was memorable for:

_____
_____
_____
_____

Would I like to be in a future production of this show?   **YES / NO**

If yes, which character/s would I like to play?

_____
_____

Anything I need to work on to achieve that:

_____
_____
_____

Memories

(Photos / tickets / cast list / cuttings from the programme)

(Photos / tickets / cast list /
cuttings from the programme)

The Show

Name of Show: _____

Date/s: _____

Theatre/Venue: _____

Director: _____

Musical Director (if applicable): _____

Choreographer (if applicable): _____

Watched a professional version of this show? When/Where?

_____

_____

_____

Role/s I auditioned for: _____

Anything of note about auditioning:

_____

_____

_____

_____

Character/s I played: _____

Notes on/any particular memories of the rehearsal process:

_____

_____

_____

_____

Reflections

What I learned from this director (notes I was given):

_____
_____
_____
_____

What I learned from others in the cast:

_____
_____
_____
_____

My assessment of this show and what it was memorable for:

_____
_____
_____
_____

Would I like to be in a future production of this show?   **YES / NO**

If yes, which character/s would I like to play?

_____
_____

Anything I need to work on to achieve that:

_____
_____
_____

Memories

(Photos / tickets / cast list /
cuttings from the programme)

The Show

Name of Show: _____

Date/s: _____

Theatre/Venue: _____

Director: _____

Musical Director (if applicable): _____

Choreographer (if applicable): _____

Watched a professional version of this show? When/Where?

_____

_____

_____

Role/s I auditioned for: _____

Anything of note about auditioning:

_____

_____

_____

_____

Character/s I played: _____

Notes on/any particular memories of the rehearsal process:

_____

_____

_____

_____

Reflections

What I learned from this director (notes I was given):

_____

_____

_____

_____

What I learned from others in the cast:

_____

_____

_____

_____

My assessment of this show and what it was memorable for:

_____

_____

_____

_____

Would I like to be in a future production of this show?   **YES / NO**

If yes, which character/s would I like to play?

_____

_____

Anything I need to work on to achieve that:

_____

_____

_____

Memories

(Photos / tickets / cast list / cuttings from the programme)

The Show

Name of Show: _____

Date/s: _____

Theatre/Venue: _____

Director: _____

Musical Director (if applicable): _____

Choreographer (if applicable): _____

Watched a professional version of this show? When/Where?

_____

_____

_____

Role/s I auditioned for: _____

Anything of note about auditioning:

_____

_____

_____

_____

Character/s I played: _____

Notes on/any particular memories of the rehearsal process:

_____

_____

_____

_____

# Reflections

What I learned from this director (notes I was given):

_____

_____

_____

_____

What I learned from others in the cast:

_____

_____

_____

_____

My assessment of this show and what it was memorable for:

_____

_____

_____

_____

Would I like to be in a future production of this show?   **YES / NO**

If yes, which character/s would I like to play?

_____

_____

Anything I need to work on to achieve that:

_____

_____

_____

Memories

(Photos / tickets / cast list /
cuttings from the programme)

The Show

Name of Show: _____

Date/s: _____

Theatre/Venue: _____

Director: _____

Musical Director (if applicable): _____

Choreographer (if applicable): _____

Watched a professional version of this show? When/Where?

_____

_____

_____

Role/s I auditioned for: _____

Anything of note about auditioning:

_____

_____

_____

_____

Character/s I played: _____

Notes on/any particular memories of the rehearsal process:

_____

_____

_____

_____

Reflections

What I learned from this director (notes I was given):

_____

_____

_____

_____

What I learned from others in the cast:

_____

_____

_____

_____

My assessment of this show and what it was memorable for:

_____

_____

_____

_____

Would I like to be in a future production of this show?   **YES / NO**

If yes, which character/s would I like to play?

_____

_____

Anything I need to work on to achieve that:

_____

_____

_____

Memories

(Photos / tickets / cast list / cuttings from the programme)

(Photos / tickets / cast list /
cuttings from the programme)

The Show

Name of Show: _____

Date/s: _____

Theatre/Venue: _____

Director: _____

Musical Director (if applicable): _____

Choreographer (if applicable): _____

Watched a professional version of this show? When/Where?

_____

_____

_____

Role/s I auditioned for: _____

Anything of note about auditioning:

_____

_____

_____

_____

Character/s I played: _____

Notes on/any particular memories of the rehearsal process:

_____

_____

_____

_____

Reflections

What I learned from this director (notes I was given):

_____

_____

_____

_____

What I learned from others in the cast:

_____

_____

_____

_____

My assessment of this show and what it was memorable for:

_____

_____

_____

_____

Would I like to be in a future production of this show?   **YES / NO**

If yes, which character/s would I like to play?

_____

_____

Anything I need to work on to achieve that:

_____

_____

_____

Memories

Memories

The Show

Name of Show: _____

Date/s: _____

Theatre/Venue: _____

Director: _____

Musical Director (if applicable): _____

Choreographer (if applicable): _____

Watched a professional version of this show? When/Where?

_____

_____

_____

Role/s I auditioned for: _____

Anything of note about auditioning:

_____

_____

_____

_____

Character/s I played: _____

Notes on/any particular memories of the rehearsal process:

_____

_____

_____

_____

Reflections

What I learned from this director (notes I was given):

_____

_____

_____

_____

What I learned from others in the cast:

_____

_____

_____

_____

My assessment of this show and what it was memorable for:

_____

_____

_____

_____

Would I like to be in a future production of this show?   **YES / NO**

If yes, which character/s would I like to play?

_____

_____

Anything I need to work on to achieve that:

_____

_____

_____

Memories

(Photos / tickets / cast list / cuttings from the programme)

(Photos / tickets / cast list /
cuttings from the programme)

The Show

Name of Show: _____

Date/s: _____

Theatre/Venue: _____

Director: _____

Musical Director (if applicable): _____

Choreographer (if applicable): _____

Watched a professional version of this show? When/Where?

_____

_____

_____

Role/s I auditioned for: _____

Anything of note about auditioning:

_____

_____

_____

_____

Character/s I played: _____

Notes on/any particular memories of the rehearsal process:

_____

_____

_____

_____

Reflections

What I learned from this director (notes I was given):

_____

_____

_____

_____

What I learned from others in the cast:

_____

_____

_____

_____

My assessment of this show and what it was memorable for:

_____

_____

_____

_____

Would I like to be in a future production of this show?   **YES / NO**

If yes, which character/s would I like to play?

_____

_____

Anything I need to work on to achieve that:

_____

_____

_____

Memories

(Photos / tickets / cast list / cuttings from the programme)

(Photos / tickets / cast list /
cuttings from the programme)

The Show

Name of Show: _____

Date/s: _____

Theatre/Venue: _____

Director: _____

Musical Director (if applicable): _____

Choreographer (if applicable): _____

Watched a professional version of this show? When/Where?

_____

_____

_____

Role/s I auditioned for: _____

Anything of note about auditioning:

_____

_____

_____

_____

Character/s I played: _____

Notes on/any particular memories of the rehearsal process:

_____

_____

_____

_____

Reflections

What I learned from this director (notes I was given):

_____

_____

_____

_____

What I learned from others in the cast:

_____

_____

_____

_____

My assessment of this show and what it was memorable for:

_____

_____

_____

_____

Would I like to be in a future production of this show?   **YES / NO**

If yes, which character/s would I like to play?

_____

_____

Anything I need to work on to achieve that:

_____

_____

_____

Memories

(Photos / tickets / cast list / cuttings from the programme)

(Photos / tickets / cast list /
cuttings from the programme)

The Show

Name of Show: _____

Date/s: _____

Theatre/Venue: _____

Director: _____

Musical Director (if applicable): _____

Choreographer (if applicable): _____

Watched a professional version of this show? When/Where?

_____

_____

_____

Role/s I auditioned for: _____

Anything of note about auditioning:

_____

_____

_____

_____

Character/s I played: _____

Notes on/any particular memories of the rehearsal process:

_____

_____

_____

_____

Reflections

What I learned from this director (notes I was given):

_____

_____

_____

_____

What I learned from others in the cast:

_____

_____

_____

_____

My assessment of this show and what it was memorable for:

_____

_____

_____

_____

Would I like to be in a future production of this show?   **YES / NO**

If yes, which character/s would I like to play?

_____

_____

Anything I need to work on to achieve that:

_____

_____

Memories

(Photos / tickets / cast list / cuttings from the programme)

(Photos / tickets / cast list / cuttings from the programme)

The Show

Name of Show: _____

Date/s: _____

Theatre/Venue: _____

Director: _____

Musical Director (if applicable): _____

Choreographer (if applicable): _____

Watched a professional version of this show? When/Where?

_____

_____

_____

Role/s I auditioned for: _____

Anything of note about auditioning:

_____

_____

_____

_____

Character/s I played: _____

Notes on/any particular memories of the rehearsal process:

_____

_____

_____

_____

Reflections

What I learned from this director (notes I was given):

_____

_____

_____

_____

What I learned from others in the cast:

_____

_____

_____

_____

My assessment of this show and what it was memorable for:

_____

_____

_____

_____

Would I like to be in a future production of this show?   **YES / NO**

If yes, which character/s would I like to play?

_____

_____

Anything I need to work on to achieve that:

_____

_____

_____

Memories

(Photos / tickets / cast list / cuttings from the programme)

Memories

The Show

Name of Show: _____

Date/s: _____

Theatre/Venue: _____

Director: _____

Musical Director (if applicable): _____

Choreographer (if applicable): _____

Watched a professional version of this show? When/Where?

_____

_____

_____

Role/s I auditioned for: _____

Anything of note about auditioning:

_____

_____

_____

_____

Character/s I played: _____

Notes on/any particular memories of the rehearsal process:

_____

_____

_____

_____

Reflections

What I learned from this director (notes I was given):

_____

_____

_____

_____

What I learned from others in the cast:

_____

_____

_____

_____

My assessment of this show and what it was memorable for:

_____

_____

_____

_____

Would I like to be in a future production of this show?   **YES / NO**

If yes, which character/s would I like to play?

_____

_____

Anything I need to work on to achieve that:

_____

_____

_____

Memories

(Photos / tickets / cast list / cuttings from the programme)

(Photos / tickets / cast list / cuttings from the programme)

The Show

Name of Show: _____

Date/s: _____

Theatre/Venue: _____

Director: _____

Musical Director (if applicable): _____

Choreographer (if applicable): _____

Watched a professional version of this show? When/Where?

_____

_____

_____

Role/s I auditioned for: _____

Anything of note about auditioning:

_____

_____

_____

_____

Character/s I played: _____

Notes on/any particular memories of the rehearsal process:

_____

_____

_____

_____

Reflections

What I learned from this director (notes I was given):

_____
_____
_____
_____

What I learned from others in the cast:

_____
_____
_____
_____

My assessment of this show and what it was memorable for:

_____
_____
_____
_____

Would I like to be in a future production of this show?   **YES / NO**

If yes, which character/s would I like to play?

_____
_____

Anything I need to work on to achieve that:

_____
_____
_____

Memories

(Photos / tickets / cast list / cuttings from the programme)

(Photos / tickets / cast list / cuttings from the programme)

The Show

Name of Show: _____

Date/s: _____

Theatre/Venue: _____

Director: _____

Musical Director (if applicable): _____

Choreographer (if applicable): _____

Watched a professional version of this show? When/Where?

_____

_____

_____

Role/s I auditioned for: _____

Anything of note about auditioning:

_____

_____

_____

_____

Character/s I played: _____

Notes on/any particular memories of the rehearsal process:

_____

_____

_____

_____

Reflections

What I learned from this director (notes I was given):

_____

_____

_____

_____

What I learned from others in the cast:

_____

_____

_____

_____

My assessment of this show and what it was memorable for:

_____

_____

_____

_____

Would I like to be in a future production of this show?   **YES / NO**

If yes, which character/s would I like to play?

_____

_____

Anything I need to work on to achieve that:

_____

_____

_____

Memories

(Photos / tickets / cast list / cuttings from the programme)

(Photos / tickets / cast list /
cuttings from the programme)

The Show

Name of Show: _____

Date/s: _____

Theatre/Venue: _____

Director: _____

Musical Director (if applicable): _____

Choreographer (if applicable): _____

Watched a professional version of this show? When/Where?

_____

_____

_____

Role/s I auditioned for: _____

Anything of note about auditioning:

_____

_____

_____

_____

Character/s I played: _____

Notes on/any particular memories of the rehearsal process:

_____

_____

_____

_____

Reflections

What I learned from this director (notes I was given):

_____

_____

_____

_____

What I learned from others in the cast:

_____

_____

_____

_____

My assessment of this show and what it was memorable for:

_____

_____

_____

_____

Would I like to be in a future production of this show?   **YES / NO**

If yes, which character/s would I like to play?

_____

_____

Anything I need to work on to achieve that:

_____

_____

_____

Memories

(Photos / tickets / cast list / cuttings from the programme)

(Photos / tickets / cast list /
cuttings from the programme)

The Show

Name of Show: _____

Date/s: _____

Theatre/Venue: _____

Director: _____

Musical Director (if applicable): _____

Choreographer (if applicable): _____

Watched a professional version of this show? When/Where?

_____

_____

_____

Role/s I auditioned for: _____

Anything of note about auditioning:

_____

_____

_____

_____

Character/s I played: _____

Notes on/any particular memories of the rehearsal process:

_____

_____

_____

_____

Reflections

What I learned from this director (notes I was given):

_____

_____

_____

_____

What I learned from others in the cast:

_____

_____

_____

_____

My assessment of this show and what it was memorable for:

_____

_____

_____

_____

Would I like to be in a future production of this show?   **YES / NO**

If yes, which character/s would I like to play?

_____

_____

Anything I need to work on to achieve that:

_____

_____

_____

Memories

(Photos / tickets / cast list / cuttings from the programme)

(Photos / tickets / cast list / cuttings from the programme)

The Show

Name of Show: _____

Date/s: _____

Theatre/Venue: _____

Director: _____

Musical Director (if applicable): _____

Choreographer (if applicable): _____

Watched a professional version of this show? When/Where?

_____

_____

_____

Role/s I auditioned for: _____

Anything of note about auditioning:

_____

_____

_____

_____

Character/s I played: _____

Notes on/any particular memories of the rehearsal process:

_____

_____

_____

_____

Reflections

What I learned from this director (notes I was given):

_____

_____

_____

_____

What I learned from others in the cast:

_____

_____

_____

_____

My assessment of this show and what it was memorable for:

_____

_____

_____

_____

Would I like to be in a future production of this show?   **YES / NO**

If yes, which character/s would I like to play?

_____

_____

Anything I need to work on to achieve that:

_____

_____

_____

Memories

(Photos / tickets / cast list / cuttings from the programme)

(Photos / tickets / cast list /
cuttings from the programme)

The Show

Name of Show: _____

Date/s: _____

Theatre/Venue: _____

Director: _____

Musical Director (if applicable): _____

Choreographer (if applicable): _____

Watched a professional version of this show? When/Where?

_____

_____

_____

Role/s I auditioned for: _____

Anything of note about auditioning:

_____

_____

_____

_____

Character/s I played: _____

Notes on/any particular memories of the rehearsal process:

_____

_____

_____

_____

Reflections

What I learned from this director (notes I was given):

_____

_____

_____

_____

What I learned from others in the cast:

_____

_____

_____

_____

My assessment of this show and what it was memorable for:

_____

_____

_____

_____

Would I like to be in a future production of this show?   **YES / NO**

If yes, which character/s would I like to play?

_____

_____

Anything I need to work on to achieve that:

_____

_____

_____

Memories

(Photos / tickets / cast list / cuttings from the programme)

(Photos / tickets / cast list /
cuttings from the programme)

The Show

Name of Show: _____

Date/s: _____

Theatre/Venue: _____

Director: _____

Musical Director (if applicable): _____

Choreographer (if applicable): _____

Watched a professional version of this show? When/Where?

_____

_____

_____

Role/s I auditioned for: _____

Anything of note about auditioning:

_____

_____

_____

_____

Character/s I played: _____

Notes on/any particular memories of the rehearsal process:

_____

_____

_____

_____

Reflections

What I learned from this director (notes I was given):

_____

_____

_____

_____

What I learned from others in the cast:

_____

_____

_____

_____

My assessment of this show and what it was memorable for:

_____

_____

_____

_____

Would I like to be in a future production of this show?   **YES / NO**

If yes, which character/s would I like to play?

_____

_____

Anything I need to work on to achieve that:

_____

_____

_____

Memories

(Photos / tickets / cast list / cuttings from the programme)

(Photos / tickets / cast list /
cuttings from the programme)

Memories

The Show

Name of Show: _____

Date/s: _____

Theatre/Venue: _____

Director: _____

Musical Director (if applicable): _____

Choreographer (if applicable): _____

Watched a professional version of this show? When/Where?

_____

_____

_____

Role/s I auditioned for: _____

Anything of note about auditioning:

_____

_____

_____

_____

Character/s I played: _____

Notes on/any particular memories of the rehearsal process:

_____

_____

_____

_____

Reflections

What I learned from this director (notes I was given):

_____

_____

_____

_____

What I learned from others in the cast:

_____

_____

_____

_____

My assessment of this show and what it was memorable for:

_____

_____

_____

_____

Would I like to be in a future production of this show? **YES / NO**

If yes, which character/s would I like to play?

_____

_____

Anything I need to work on to achieve that:

_____

_____

_____

Memories

(Photos / tickets / cast list / cuttings from the programme)

Memories

The Show

Name of Show: _____

Date/s: _____

Theatre/Venue: _____

Director: _____

Musical Director (if applicable): _____

Choreographer (if applicable): _____

Watched a professional version of this show? When/Where?

_____

_____

_____

Role/s I auditioned for: _____

Anything of note about auditioning:

_____

_____

_____

_____

Character/s I played: _____

Notes on/any particular memories of the rehearsal process:

_____

_____

_____

_____

Reflections

What I learned from this director (notes I was given):

_____
_____
_____
_____

What I learned from others in the cast:

_____
_____
_____
_____

My assessment of this show and what it was memorable for:

_____
_____
_____
_____

Would I like to be in a future production of this show? **YES / NO**

If yes, which character/s would I like to play?

_____
_____

Anything I need to work on to achieve that:

_____
_____
_____

Memories

(Photos / tickets / cast list / cuttings from the programme)

(Photos / tickets / cast list /
cuttings from the programme)

Memories

The Show

Name of Show: _____

Date/s: _____

Theatre/Venue: _____

Director: _____

Musical Director (if applicable): _____

Choreographer (if applicable): _____

Watched a professional version of this show? When/Where?

_____

_____

_____

Role/s I auditioned for: _____

Anything of note about auditioning:

_____

_____

_____

Character/s I played: _____

Notes on/any particular memories of the rehearsal process:

_____

_____

_____

_____

Reflections

What I learned from this director (notes I was given):

_____

_____

_____

_____

What I learned from others in the cast:

_____

_____

_____

_____

My assessment of this show and what it was memorable for:

_____

_____

_____

_____

Would I like to be in a future production of this show?   **YES / NO**

If yes, which character/s would I like to play?

_____

_____

Anything I need to work on to achieve that:

_____

_____

_____

Memories

(Photos / tickets / cast list / cuttings from the programme)

(Photos / tickets / cast list / cuttings from the programme)

Memories

Made in United States
Troutdale, OR
12/05/2024

25979214R00064